Amazon Sun, Amazon Rain

by Ximena de la Piedra

SCHOLASTIC INC.
New York   Toronto   London   Auckland   Sydney

Copyright © 1994 by Scholastic Inc.
All rights reserved. Published by Scholastic Inc.
Printed in the U.S.A.
ISBN 0-590-27364-7
ISBN 0-590-29212-9 (meets NASTA specifications)

2 3 4 5 6 7 8 9 10   08   01 00 99 98 97 96 95 94

The hot sun warms the Amazon jungle.

All morning long . . .

4

mosquitos buzz and hum.

Butterflies fly to and fro.

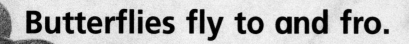

Monkeys swing in the tall trees.

Birds chit-chat.

8

Frogs nap under giant leaves.

9

Turtles sit in the sun.

By noon, clouds gather.

Soon the CRASH and BOOM of thunder shakes the jungle.
Lightning fills the sky.

Suddenly, it's raining.

The mosquitos stop buzzing.
The butterflies are still.
The monkeys hide under the dripping leaves.

The birds rush to their nests.
The frogs jump from puddle to puddle.
The turtles dive into the river.

Then the rain stops.
One by one the animals come back out.
Once again the hot sun
warms the Amazon jungle.